This journal belongs to

_____

"Hope begins in the dark,
the stubborn hope that if you show up and try to do
the right thing, the dawn will come."
"You wait and watch and work:
you don't give up."

— *Anne Lamott*

365 days • 3 years • 1095 answers

Q & A -3-year Journal for Christians
Copyright © 2018 by Lina AbuJamra
ISBN 978-0-9897387-2-9

Published by Paladin Publishers
P. O. Box 700515
Tulsa, OK 74170

Represented by PriorityPR Group & Literary Agency.
www.prioritypr.org
Text Design/Layout: Lisa Simpson

Published in the United States
Printed in Canada

❖ January ❖

1

WHAT IS YOUR WORD FOR THE UPCOMING YEAR?

20___: _____

_____

_____

_____

•◆•

20___: _____

_____

_____

_____

•◆•

20___: _____

_____

_____

_____

•◆•

❖ **January** ❖

What is your biggest regret right now?

20__: _____

_____

_____

_____

•◆•

20__: _____

_____

_____

_____

•◆•

20__: _____

_____

_____

_____

•◆•

WHAT IS YOUR BIBLE READING PLAN FOR THE YEAR?

20___: _____

_____

_____

_____

•◆•

20___: _____

_____

_____

_____

•◆•

20___: _____

_____

_____

_____

•◆•

❖ January ❖

WHAT IS YOUR GREATEST RELATIONSHIP STRESS RIGHT NOW?

20___: _____

_____

_____

_____

•◆•

20___: _____

_____

_____

_____

•◆•

20___: _____

_____

_____

_____

•◆•

❖ January ❖

5

THE BEST PART OF TODAY WAS?

20__: _____

_____

_____

_____

•◆•

20__: _____

_____

_____

_____

•◆•

20__: _____

_____

_____

_____

•◆•

WHAT'S ON YOUR BUCKET LIST FOR THIS UPCOMING YEAR?

20__: _____

_____

_____

_____

• ◆ •

20__: _____

_____

_____

_____

• ◆ •

20__: _____

_____

_____

_____

• ◆ •

WHAT'S YOUR FAVORITE VERSE IN THIS SEASON OF LIFE?

20___: _____

_____

_____

_____

•◆•

20___: _____

_____

_____

_____

•◆•

20___: _____

_____

_____

_____

•◆•

IN WHAT SPECIFIC WAY HAS GOD CHANGED YOU LATELY?

20__: _____

_____

_____

_____

•◆•

20__: _____

_____

_____

_____

•◆•

20__: _____

_____

_____

_____

•◆•

WHO DO YOU NEED TO ASK FORGIVENESS OF?

20__: _____

_____

_____

_____

• ◆ •

20__: _____

_____

_____

_____

• ◆ •

20__: _____

_____

_____

_____

• ◆ •

10 ❖ January ❖

WHAT DO YOU NEED TO LET GO OF?

20__: _____

_____

_____

_____

•◆•

20__: _____

_____

_____

_____

•◆•

20__: _____

_____

_____

_____

•◆•

WRITE WHAT GOD HAS DONE FOR YOU IN A SENTENCE.

20__: _____

_____

_____

_____

•◆•

20__: _____

_____

_____

_____

•◆•

20__: _____

_____

_____

_____

•◆•

12 ❖ January ❖

WHAT NEW VENTURE HAS GOD CALLED YOU TO THIS YEAR?

20__: _____

_____

_____

_____

•◆•

20__: _____

_____

_____

_____

•◆•

20__: _____

_____

_____

_____

•◆•

WHO'S YOUR FAVORITE BIBLE CHARACTER RIGHT NOW?

20___: _____

_____

_____

_____

•◆•

20___: _____

_____

_____

_____

•◆•

20___: _____

_____

_____

_____

•◆•

14 ❖ January ❖

WHAT WOULD YOU LIKE TO FIND OUT MORE ABOUT GOD?

20__: _____

_____

_____

_____

• ◆ •

20__: _____

_____

_____

_____

• ◆ •

20__: _____

_____

_____

_____

• ◆ •

❖ January ❖ 15

DESCRIBE GOD IN A FEW WORDS.

20__: _____

_____

_____

_____

•◆•

20__: _____

_____

_____

_____

•◆•

20__: _____

_____

_____

_____

•◆•

16 ❖ January ❖

WHO IS YOUR PRAYER PARTNER?

20__: _____

_____

_____

_____

•◆•

20__: _____

_____

_____

_____

•◆•

20__: _____

_____

_____

_____

•◆•

❖ January ❖ 17

WHAT IS THE TOP ITEM ON YOUR PRAYER LIST RIGHT NOW?

20__: _____

_____

_____

_____

•◆•

20__: _____

_____

_____

_____

•◆•

20__: _____

_____

_____

_____

•◆•

18 ❖ January ❖

WHERE ARE YOU GOING TO CHURCH?

20__: _____

_____

_____

_____

• ◆ •

20__: _____

_____

_____

_____

• ◆ •

20__: _____

_____

_____

_____

• ◆ •

WHAT'S THE LAST VERSE OF SCRIPTURE YOU MEMORIZED?

20___: _____

_____

_____

_____

•◆•

20___: _____

_____

_____

_____

•◆•

20___: _____

_____

_____

_____

•◆•

 **January**

TODAY WAS TOUGH BECAUSE _____.

20__: _____
_____
_____
_____

• ◆ •

20__: _____
_____
_____
_____

• ◆ •

20__: _____
_____
_____
_____

• ◆ •

❖ January ❖ 21

WHAT IS YOUR FAVORITE WORSHIP SONG?

20__: _____

_____

_____

_____

●◆●

20__: _____

_____

_____

_____

●◆●

20__: _____

_____

_____

_____

●◆●

 ❖ January ❖

WHAT DO YOU STILL LONG TO DO
FOR THE LORD?

20__: _____

_____

_____

_____

• ◆ •

20__: _____

_____

_____

_____

• ◆ •

20__: _____

_____

_____

_____

• ◆ •

❖ January ❖ 23

WHO DID YOU IMPACT WITH KINDNESS TODAY?

20___: _____

_____

_____

_____

•◆•

20___: _____

_____

_____

_____

•◆•

20___: _____

_____

_____

_____

•◆•

24 ❖ January ❖

HOW ARE YOU FEELING TODAY?

20__: _____

_____

_____

_____

•◆•

20__: _____

_____

_____

_____

•◆•

20__: _____

_____

_____

_____

•◆•

❖ January ❖ **25**

HAVE YOU PRAYED WITH ANYONE TODAY?

20__: _____

_____

_____

_____

• ◆ •

20__: _____

_____

_____

_____

• ◆ •

20__: _____

_____

_____

_____

• ◆ •

 **❖ January ❖**

WHAT IS THE LAST THING
YOU WASTED YOUR MONEY ON?

20__: _____

_____

_____

_____

•◆•

20__: _____

_____

_____

_____

•◆•

20__: _____

_____

_____

_____

•◆•

❖ January ❖ 27

WHAT BOOK ARE YOU READING RIGHT NOW?

20__: _____

_____

_____

_____

•◆•

20__: _____

_____

_____

_____

•◆•

20__: _____

_____

_____

_____

•◆•

 **28** ❖ January ❖

WHO WAS THE LAST PERSON YOU TOLD ABOUT JESUS?

20___: _____

_____

_____

_____

•◆•

20___: _____

_____

_____

_____

•◆•

20___: _____

_____

_____

_____

•◆•

IF YOU COULD GO ON A MISSION TRIP, YOU WOULD GO TO _____.

20__: _____

_____

_____

_____

• ◆ •

20__: _____

_____

_____

_____

• ◆ •

20__: _____

_____

_____

_____

• ◆ •

30 ❖ January ❖

THE BIGGEST HABIT YOU WISH YOU COULD BREAK IS _____.

20__: _____
_____
_____
_____

•◆•

20__: _____
_____
_____
_____

•◆•

20__: _____
_____
_____
_____

•◆•

YOUR FAVORITE CHRISTIAN AUTHOR IS

_____.

20__: _____

_____

_____

_____

•◆•

20__: _____

_____

_____

_____

•◆•

20__: _____

_____

_____

_____

•◆•

1

❖ February ❖

WHAT IS YOUR NEXT BIG PROJECT?

20___: _____

_____

_____

_____

•◆•

20___: _____

_____

_____

_____

•◆•

20___: _____

_____

_____

_____

•◆•

❖ February ❖

WHICH DISCIPLINE IN THE CHRISTIAN LIFE DO YOU STRUGGLE WITH THE MOST?

20__: _____

_____

_____

_____

•◆•

20__: _____

_____

_____

_____

•◆•

20__: _____

_____

_____

_____

•◆•

3

WHAT IS YOUR FAVORITE THING TO DO?

20__: _____

_____

_____

_____

•◆•

20__: _____

_____

_____

_____

•◆•

20__: _____

_____

_____

_____

•◆•

WHO IS YOUR FAVORITE PREACHER TO LISTEN TO?

20__: _____

_____

_____

_____

●◆●

20__: _____

_____

_____

_____

●◆●

20__: _____

_____

_____

_____

●◆●

❖ February ❖

WHAT IS THE LAST BIBLE STUDY YOU DID?

20__: _____

_____

_____

_____

• ◆ •

20__: _____

_____

_____

_____

• ◆ •

20__: _____

_____

_____

_____

• ◆ •

❖ February ❖

WHAT TELEVISION SHOWS ARE YOU WATCHING RIGHT NOW?

20__: _____

_____

_____

_____

•◆•

20__: _____

_____

_____

_____

•◆•

20__: _____

_____

_____

_____

•◆•

7

**IF YOU WERE TO PICK ONE ACTIVITY
TO DO ALL DAY, YOU WOULD _____.**

20__: _____

_____

_____

_____

•◆•

20__: _____

_____

_____

_____

•◆•

20__: _____

_____

_____

_____

•◆•

❖ February ❖

HOW IS YOUR RELATIONSHIP WITH YOUR BOSS?

20__: _____

_____

_____

_____

•◆•

20__: _____

_____

_____

_____

•◆•

20__: _____

_____

_____

_____

•◆•

❖ February ❖

HOW WOULD WORKMATES DESCRIBE YOUR MOOD THESE DAYS?

20__: _____

_____

_____

_____

•◆•

20__: _____

_____

_____

_____

•◆•

20__: _____

_____

_____

_____

•◆•

❖ February ❖ 10

WHAT DO YOU HOPE NO ONE EVER FINDS OUT ABOUT YOU?

20__: _____

_____

_____

_____

•◆•

20__: _____

_____

_____

_____

•◆•

20__: _____

_____

_____

_____

•◆•

11 ❖ February ❖

WHAT DID YOU COOK LAST?

20__: _____

_____

_____

_____

• ◆ •

20__: _____

_____

_____

_____

• ◆ •

20__: _____

_____

_____

_____

• ◆ •

❖ February ❖ 12

WHEN IS THE LAST TIME YOU WENT ON A DATE?

20__: _____

_____

_____

_____

• ◆ •

20__: _____

_____

_____

_____

• ◆ •

20__: _____

_____

_____

_____

• ◆ •

13 ❖ February ❖

HOW MUCH MONEY DID YOU SAVE THIS MONTH?

20___: _____
_____
_____
_____

•◆•

20___: _____
_____
_____
_____

•◆•

20___: _____
_____
_____
_____

•◆•

WHEN WAS THE LAST TIME YOU FELT TRUE PEACE?

20___: _____

_____

_____

_____

•◆•

20___: _____

_____

_____

_____

•◆•

20___: _____

_____

_____

_____

•◆•

15 ❖ February ❖

WHAT'S THE BIGGEST BATTLE YOU'RE IN RIGHT NOW?

20__: _____

_____

_____

_____

•◆•

20__: _____

_____

_____

_____

•◆•

20__: _____

_____

_____

_____

•◆•

LAST SPECIFIC ANSWER TO PRAYER.

20__: _____

_____

_____

_____

•◆•

20__: _____

_____

_____

_____

•◆•

20__: _____

_____

_____

_____

•◆•

17 ❖ February ❖

DESCRIBE YOURSELF IN ONE SENTENCE.

20__: _____

_____

_____

_____

• ◆ •

20__: _____

_____

_____

_____

• ◆ •

20__: _____

_____

_____

_____

• ◆ •

❖ February ❖ 18

WHERE WAS THE LAST SELFIE YOU TOOK?

20__: _____

_____

_____

_____

•◆•

20__: _____

_____

_____

_____

•◆•

20__: _____

_____

_____

_____

•◆•

19 ❖ February ❖

HOW ARE YOU PRESENTLY INVOLVED
IN YOUR LOCAL CHURCH?

20__: _____

_____

_____

_____

• ◆ •

20__: _____

_____

_____

_____

• ◆ •

20__: _____

_____

_____

_____

• ◆ •

❖ February ❖

WHAT'S YOUR FAVORITE
TYPE OF DRINKING WATER?

20__: _____

_____

_____

_____

• ◆ •

20__: _____

_____

_____

_____

• ◆ •

20__: _____

_____

_____

_____

• ◆ •

21 ❖ February ❖

DO YOU KNOW ANY WIDOWS OR ORPHANS PERSONALLY?

20__: _____

_____

_____

_____

• ◆ •

20__: _____

_____

_____

_____

• ◆ •

20__: _____

_____

_____

_____

• ◆ •

❖ February ❖

DESCRIBE YOUR RELATIONSHIP WITH YOUR FAMILY IN THREE WORDS.

20__: _____

_____

_____

_____

• ◆ •

20__: _____

_____

_____

_____

• ◆ •

20__: _____

_____

_____

_____

• ◆ •

23 ❖ February ❖

LAST COUNTRY YOU VISITED.

20__: _____

_____

_____

_____

•◆•

20__: _____

_____

_____

_____

•◆•

20__: _____

_____

_____

_____

•◆•

❖ February ❖

WHAT BOOK WOULD YOU LIKE TO READ?

20__: _____

_____

_____

_____

•◆•

20__: _____

_____

_____

_____

•◆•

20__: _____

_____

_____

_____

•◆•

25 ❖ February ❖

IF YOU WERE TO HANG OUT WITH ONE BIBLE CHARACTER, WHO WOULD IT BE?

20__: _____

_____

_____

_____

• ◆ •

20__: _____

_____

_____

_____

• ◆ •

20__: _____

_____

_____

_____

• ◆ •

❖ February ❖ 26

WHAT IS YOUR FAVORITE FLOWER?

20___: _____

_____

_____

•◆•

20___: _____

_____

_____

•◆•

20___: _____

_____

_____

•◆•

27 ❖ February ❖

WHAT'S THE LAST RESTAURANT YOU ATE AT?

20__: _____

_____

_____

_____

•◆•

20__: _____

_____

_____

_____

•◆•

20__: _____

_____

_____

_____

•◆•

❖ February ❖

WHERE WAS THE LAST TIME YOU SPENT TIME OUTDOORS?

20__: _____

_____

_____

_____

•◆•

20__: _____

_____

_____

_____

•◆•

20__: _____

_____

_____

_____

•◆•

1

WHEN WAS THE LAST TIME YOU SENSED GOD SPEAKING TO YOU?

20__: _____

_____

_____

_____

• ◆ •

20__: _____

_____

_____

_____

• ◆ •

20__: _____

_____

_____

_____

• ◆ •

WHEN WAS THE LAST TIME YOU SPOKE TO GOD?

20__: _____

_____

_____

•◆•

20__: _____

_____

_____

•◆•

20__: _____

_____

_____

•◆•

❖ **March** ❖

WHO IS THE LAST PERSON YOU CALLED ON YOUR PHONE?

20__: _____

_____

_____

_____

•◆•

20__: _____

_____

_____

_____

•◆•

20__: _____

_____

_____

_____

•◆•

❖ March ❖

WHO IS YOUR BEST FRIEND?

20__: _____

_____

_____

_____

•◆•

20__: _____

_____

_____

_____

•◆•

20__: _____

_____

_____

_____

•◆•

5

❖ March ❖

WHICH CULTURE DO YOU HAVE ABSOLUTELY NO IDEA ABOUT?

20__: _____

_____

_____

_____

•◆•

20__: _____

_____

_____

_____

•◆•

20__: _____

_____

_____

_____

•◆•

❖ March ❖

WHAT IS YOUR PASTOR PREACHING ABOUT RIGHT NOW?

20___: _____

_____

_____

_____

•◆•

20___: _____

_____

_____

_____

•◆•

20___: _____

_____

_____

_____

•◆•

7

❖ March ❖

WHAT IS THE LAST THING YOU LEARNED?

20__: _____

_____

_____

_____

•◆•

20__: _____

_____

_____

_____

•◆•

20__: _____

_____

_____

_____

•◆•

❖ **March** ❖

WHAT DID YOU COMPLAIN ABOUT TODAY?

20__: _____
_____
_____
_____

• ◆ •

20__: _____
_____
_____
_____

• ◆ •

20__: _____
_____
_____
_____

• ◆ •

❖ March ❖

WHAT ARE YOU GRATEFUL FOR IN THIS MOMENT?

20__: _____

_____

_____

_____

•◆•

20__: _____

_____

_____

_____

•◆•

20__: _____

_____

_____

_____

•◆•

WHAT ARE YOUR CURRENT ADDICTIONS?

20___: _____

_____

_____

_____

● ◆ ●

20___: _____

_____

_____

_____

● ◆ ●

20___: _____

_____

_____

_____

● ◆ ●

11

❖ March ❖

WHERE DID YOU SPEND MOST OF YOUR TIME TODAY?

20__: _____

_____

_____

_____

•◆•

20__: _____

_____

_____

_____

•◆•

20__: _____

_____

_____

_____

•◆•

❖ March ❖ 12

WHAT DEVOTIONAL ARE YOU READING THROUGH RIGHT NOW?

20__: _____

_____

_____

_____

• ◆ •

20__: _____

_____

_____

_____

• ◆ •

20__: _____

_____

_____

_____

• ◆ •

13 ❖ March ❖

DESCRIBE YOUR CLOTHING STYLE NOW.

20__: _____

_____

_____

_____

•◆•

20__: _____

_____

_____

_____

•◆•

20__: _____

_____

_____

_____

•◆•

DO YOU WEAR GLASSES OR CONTACTS?

20___: _____

_____

_____

_____

•◆•

20___: _____

_____

_____

_____

•◆•

20___: _____

_____

_____

_____

•◆•

15 ❖ March ❖

IF YOU COULD CHANGE SOMETHING ABOUT THE WAY YOU LOOK, WHAT WOULD IT BE?

20__: _____

_____

_____

_____

•◆•

20__: _____

_____

_____

_____

•◆•

20__: _____

_____

_____

_____

•◆•

❖ March ❖ 16

ARE YOU A LEADER OR LISTENER?

20__: _____

_____

_____

_____

•◆•

20__: _____

_____

_____

_____

•◆•

20__: _____

_____

_____

_____

•◆•

17

❖ March ❖

WHO IS YOUR GREATEST TEACHER?

20__: _____

_____

_____

_____

• ◆ •

20__: _____

_____

_____

_____

• ◆ •

20__: _____

_____

_____

_____

• ◆ •

❖ March ❖

18

NAME YOUR ROLE MODEL.

20__: _____

_____

_____

_____

•◆•

20__: _____

_____

_____

_____

•◆•

20__: _____

_____

_____

_____

•◆•

19 ❖ March ❖

WHERE IS YOUR PRESENT WALK WITH CHRIST LEADING?

20___: _____

_____

_____

_____

•◆•

20___: _____

_____

_____

_____

•◆•

20___: _____

_____

_____

_____

•◆•

❖ March ❖

WHAT ARE YOU OBSESSED WITH RIGHT NOW?

20___: _____

_____

_____

_____

• ◆ •

20___: _____

_____

_____

_____

• ◆ •

20___: _____

_____

_____

_____

• ◆ •

21 ❖ March ❖

WHAT DO YOU CRAVE?

20___: _____

_____

_____

_____

•◆•

20___: _____

_____

_____

_____

•◆•

20___: _____

_____

_____

_____

•◆•

WHAT LEVEL OF CONVERSATION DO YOU ENGAGE IN WITH PEOPLE YOU KNOW?

20___: _____

_____

_____

_____

• ◆ •

20___: _____

_____

_____

_____

• ◆ •

20___: _____

_____

_____

_____

• ◆ •

23

❖ March ❖

_____ IS COMPLETELY
DISHONORING TO GOD.

20__: _____

_____

_____

_____

• ◆ •

20__: _____

_____

_____

_____

• ◆ •

20__: _____

_____

_____

_____

• ◆ •

WHO IS YOUR FAVORITE CHRISTIAN SPEAKER?

20__: _____

_____

_____

_____

•◆•

20__: _____

_____

_____

_____

•◆•

20__: _____

_____

_____

_____

•◆•

25 ❖ March ❖

WHAT LEVEL OF CONVERSATION DO YOU ENGAGE IN WITH PEOPLE YOU DON'T KNOW?

20__: _____

_____

_____

_____

• ◆ •

20__: _____

_____

_____

_____

• ◆ •

20__: _____

_____

_____

_____

• ◆ •

❖ March ❖

26

WHICH OF THE DISCIPLES DESCRIBES YOU?

20__: _____

_____

_____

_____

•◆•

20__: _____

_____

_____

_____

•◆•

20__: _____

_____

_____

_____

•◆•

27 ❖ March ❖

WHAT WOULD YOU LIKE
TO REMEMBER FROM TODAY?

20__: _____

_____

_____

_____

•◆•

20__: _____

_____

_____

_____

•◆•

20__: _____

_____

_____

_____

•◆•

❖ March ❖

WHAT WOULD YOU LIKE PEOPLE TO SAY ABOUT YOU AT YOUR FUNERAL?

20__: _____

_____

_____

_____

• ◆ •

20__: _____

_____

_____

_____

• ◆ •

20__: _____

_____

_____

_____

• ◆ •

❖ March ❖

WHY ARE YOU WORKING AT YOUR CURRENT JOB?

20__: _____

_____

_____

_____

• ◆ •

20__: _____

_____

_____

_____

• ◆ •

20__: _____

_____

_____

_____

• ◆ •

❖ March ❖

IS YOUR LIFE TODAY WHAT YOU THOUGHT IT WOULD BE?

20__: _____

_____

_____

_____

•◆•

20__: _____

_____

_____

_____

•◆•

20__: _____

_____

_____

_____

•◆•

31

❖ March ❖

WHAT BIG DECISION ARE YOU TRYING TO MAKE?

20__: _____

_____

_____

_____

•◆•

20__: _____

_____

_____

_____

•◆•

20__: _____

_____

_____

_____

•◆•

❖ April ❖

1

WHAT GIFTS HAS GOD GIVEN YOU?

20__: _____

_____

_____

_____

•◆•

20__: _____

_____

_____

_____

•◆•

20__: _____

_____

_____

_____

•◆•

❖ **April** ❖

WHAT DO YOU FIND BEAUTIFUL?

20___: _____

_____

_____

_____

•◆•

20___: _____

_____

_____

_____

•◆•

20___: _____

_____

_____

_____

•◆•

❖ April ❖

3

GOD'S FAVOR IS _____.

20__: _____
_____
_____
_____

•◆•

20__: _____
_____
_____
_____

•◆•

20__: _____
_____
_____
_____

•◆•

❖ **April** ❖

**I AM MOST THANKFUL FOR THIS PERSON
IN MY LIFE RIGHT NOW.**

20___: _____

_____

_____

_____

●◆●

20___: _____

_____

_____

_____

●◆●

20___: _____

_____

_____

_____

●◆●

ON A SCALE OF 1-10,
HOW GRATEFUL WERE YOU TODAY?

20__: _____

_____

_____

_____

•◆•

20__: _____

_____

_____

_____

•◆•

20__: _____

_____

_____

_____

•◆•

❖ April ❖

WHEN WAS THE LAST TIME YOU FELT CONVICTED?

20__: _____

_____

_____

_____

•◆•

20__: _____

_____

_____

_____

•◆•

20__: _____

_____

_____

_____

•◆•

IF YOU COULD WRITE A BOOK, WHAT WOULD IT BE ABOUT?

20__: _____

_____

_____

_____

•◆•

20__: _____

_____

_____

_____

•◆•

20__: _____

_____

_____

_____

•◆•

❖ April ❖

READ A BOOK BY THE FIRE OR LAY IN THE SUN?

20__: _____

_____

_____

_____

•◆•

20__: _____

_____

_____

_____

•◆•

20__: _____

_____

_____

_____

•◆•

❖ April ❖

LAST LECTURE YOU GAVE
SOMEONE WAS ON _____.

20__: _____

_____

_____

_____

•◆•

20__: _____

_____

_____

_____

•◆•

20__: _____

_____

_____

_____

•◆•

10 ❖ April ❖

WHAT'S YOUR EXERCISE ROUTINE RIGHT NOW?

20__: _____

_____

_____

_____

•◆•

20__: _____

_____

_____

_____

•◆•

20__: _____

_____

_____

_____

•◆•

❖ April ❖

11

**IF YOU COULD DO ONE THING OVER,
WHAT WOULD IT BE?**

20___: _____

_____

_____

_____

•◆•

20___: _____

_____

_____

_____

•◆•

20___: _____

_____

_____

_____

•◆•

12 ❖ April ❖

WHAT WORD DO YOU WISH YOU COULD STOP SAYING?

20__: _____

_____

_____

_____

•◆•

20__: _____

_____

_____

_____

•◆•

20__: _____

_____

_____

_____

•◆•

❖ April ❖ 13

TODAY YOU'VE GOT TOO MUCH _____.

20__: _____

_____

_____

_____

• ◆ •

20__: _____

_____

_____

_____

• ◆ •

20__: _____

_____

_____

_____

• ◆ •

14 ❖ April ❖

TOP CONTROVERSIAL ISSUES
IN YOUR CULTURE RIGHT NOW.

20__: _____

_____

_____

_____

• ◆ •

20__: _____

_____

_____

_____

• ◆ •

20__: _____

_____

_____

_____

• ◆ •

❖ April ❖ 15

DO YOU HAVE CLOSE FRIENDS OF ANOTHER RACE?

20__: _____

_____

_____

_____

•◆•

20__: _____

_____

_____

_____

•◆•

20__: _____

_____

_____

_____

•◆•

16 ❖ April ❖

DO YOU HAVE FRIENDS YOU DISAGREE WITH?

20__: _____

_____

_____

_____

• ◆ •

20__: _____

_____

_____

_____

• ◆ •

20__: _____

_____

_____

_____

• ◆ •

HOW MUCH ARE YOU TITHING?

20__: _____

_____

_____

_____

• ◆ •

20__: _____

_____

_____

_____

• ◆ •

20__: _____

_____

_____

_____

• ◆ •

18 ❖ April ❖

WRITE A MISSION STATEMENT FOR YOUR LIFE.

20__: _____
_____
_____
_____

•◆•

20__: _____
_____
_____
_____

•◆•

20__: _____
_____
_____
_____

•◆•

❖ April ❖ 19

LAST TIME YOU FELT REALLY HURT BY SOMEONE.

20__: _____

_____

_____

_____

•◆•

20__: _____

_____

_____

_____

•◆•

20__: _____

_____

_____

_____

•◆•

❖ April ❖

WHAT SEASON ARE YOU IN LIFE RIGHT NOW?

20___: _____

_____

_____

_____

• ◆ •

20___: _____

_____

_____

_____

• ◆ •

20___: _____

_____

_____

_____

• ◆ •

❖ April ❖ 21

IF YOU COULD ASK JESUS ONE QUESTION:

20___: _____

_____

_____

_____

•◆•

20___: _____

_____

_____

_____

•◆•

20___: _____

_____

_____

_____

•◆•

❖ April ❖

WHO DO YOU SEEK ADVICE FROM?

20__: _____

_____

_____

_____

•◆•

20__: _____

_____

_____

_____

•◆•

20__: _____

_____

_____

_____

•◆•

❖ April ❖

WHAT IS THE HARDEST COMMANDMENT FOR YOU TO FOLLOW?

20__: _____

_____

_____

_____

• ◆ •

20__: _____

_____

_____

_____

• ◆ •

20__: _____

_____

_____

_____

• ◆ •

24 ❖ April ❖

WHO ARE YOU SURROUNDING YOURSELF WITH?

20__: _____

_____

_____

_____

•◆•

20__: _____

_____

_____

_____

•◆•

20__: _____

_____

_____

_____

•◆•

❖ April ❖

WHAT ARE YOU SURROUNDING YOURSELF WITH?

20___: _____

_____

_____

_____

•◆•

20___: _____

_____

_____

_____

•◆•

20___: _____

_____

_____

_____

•◆•

❖ April ❖

WHEN ARE YOU READING YOUR BIBLE?

20___: _____

_____

_____

_____

•◆•

20___: _____

_____

_____

_____

•◆•

20___: _____

_____

_____

_____

•◆•

HOW OFTEN DO YOU PRAY?

20__: _____

_____

_____

_____

•◆•

20__: _____

_____

_____

_____

•◆•

20__: _____

_____

_____

_____

•◆•

❖ April ❖

WHO IS YOUR PRAYER WARRIOR?

20__: _____

_____

_____

_____

•◆•

20__: _____

_____

_____

_____

•◆•

20__: _____

_____

_____

_____

•◆•

WHO DO YOU HAVE A HARD TIME TRUSTING?

20__: _____

_____

_____

_____

• ◆ •

20__: _____

_____

_____

_____

• ◆ •

20__: _____

_____

_____

_____

• ◆ •

30 ❖ April ❖

WHO MAKES YOU LAUGH THE MOST?

20__: _____

_____

_____

_____

•◆•

20__: _____

_____

_____

_____

•◆•

20__: _____

_____

_____

_____

•◆•

❖ May ❖

1

HOW MUCH TIME
DO YOU SPEND ON TECHNOLOGY?

20__: _____

_____

_____

_____

• ◆ •

20__: _____

_____

_____

_____

• ◆ •

20__: _____

_____

_____

_____

• ◆ •

❖ May ❖

HOW IS GOD HELPING YOU IN YOUR TRIALS?

20__: _____

_____

_____

_____

•◆•

20__: _____

_____

_____

_____

•◆•

20__: _____

_____

_____

_____

•◆•

❖ May ❖

ON A SCALE FROM 1-10,
HOW HOLY DID YOU LIVE TODAY?

20___: _____

_____

_____

_____

•◆•

20___: _____

_____

_____

_____

•◆•

20___: _____

_____

_____

_____

•◆•

❖ May ❖

WHO DID YOU HAVE OVER FOR DINNER THIS WEEK?

20__: _____

_____

_____

_____

•◆•

20__: _____

_____

_____

_____

•◆•

20__: _____

_____

_____

_____

•◆•

❖ May ❖

WHAT'S THE LAST MOVIE YOU WATCHED?

20__: _____

_____

_____

_____

•◆•

20__: _____

_____

_____

_____

•◆•

20__: _____

_____

_____

_____

•◆•

❖ May ❖

WHICH AUTHORITY FIGURE DO YOU STRUGGLE OBEYING?

20___: _____

_____

_____

_____

•◆•

20___: _____

_____

_____

_____

•◆•

20___: _____

_____

_____

_____

•◆•

❖ May ❖

WRITE THE FIRST SENTENCE OF YOUR AUTOBIOGRAPHY.

20__: _____

_____

_____

_____

•◆•

20__: _____

_____

_____

_____

•◆•

20__: _____

_____

_____

_____

•◆•

❖ May ❖

WHAT IS YOUR FAVORITE CHRISTIAN BAND?

20__: _____

_____

_____

_____

•◆•

20__: _____

_____

_____

_____

•◆•

20__: _____

_____

_____

_____

•◆•

❖ May ❖

WHICH BIBLE CHAPTER
DO YOU KEEP GOING BACK TO?

20___: _____

_____

_____

_____

●◆●

20___: _____

_____

_____

_____

●◆●

20___: _____

_____

_____

_____

●◆●

10 ❖ May ❖

WHAT ENCOURAGES YOU THE MOST?

20___: _____

_____

_____

_____

•◆•

20___: _____

_____

_____

_____

•◆•

20___: _____

_____

_____

_____

•◆•

❖ May ❖

11

WHAT'S YOUR LOVE LANGUAGE?

20__: _____

_____

_____

_____

●◆●

20__: _____

_____

_____

_____

●◆●

20__: _____

_____

_____

_____

●◆●

12

❖ May ❖

WHAT SPIRITUAL GIFT DO YOU WISH YOU HAD?

20__: _____

_____

_____

_____

•◆•

20__: _____

_____

_____

_____

•◆•

20__: _____

_____

_____

_____

•◆•

DO YOU FEEL THE HOLY SPIRIT'S PRESENCE IN YOU?

20__: _____

_____

_____

_____

•◆•

20__: _____

_____

_____

_____

•◆•

20__: _____

_____

_____

_____

•◆•

14

❖ May ❖

WHAT HAS GROWN YOUR FAITH IN THIS SEASON?

20__: _____

_____

_____

_____

•◆•

20__: _____

_____

_____

_____

•◆•

20__: _____

_____

_____

_____

•◆•

❖ May ❖

15

WHAT MAKES YOU FEEL TIRED?

20__: _____

_____

_____

_____

• ◆ •

20__: _____

_____

_____

_____

• ◆ •

20__: _____

_____

_____

_____

• ◆ •

16 ❖ May ❖

LAST THING YOU SURRENDERED TO JESUS.

20__: _____

_____

_____

_____

•◆•

20__: _____

_____

_____

_____

•◆•

20__: _____

_____

_____

_____

•◆•

❖ May ❖

17

WHAT IS YOUR GOD-GIVEN PURPOSE?

20__: _____

_____

_____

_____

•◆•

20__: _____

_____

_____

_____

•◆•

20__: _____

_____

_____

_____

•◆•

18 ❖ May ❖

WHEN WAS THE LAST TIME YOU CRIED?

20__: _____

_____

_____

_____

•◆•

20__: _____

_____

_____

_____

•◆•

20__: _____

_____

_____

_____

•◆•

❖ May ❖ 19

YOU FEEL MOST GUILTY WHEN YOU _____.

20__: _____

_____

_____

_____

•◆•

20__: _____

_____

_____

_____

•◆•

20__: _____

_____

_____

_____

•◆•

 ❖ May ❖

PRACTICES THAT HELP YOU OVERCOME ANXIETY.

20__: _____

_____

_____

_____

•◆•

20__: _____

_____

_____

_____

•◆•

20__: _____

_____

_____

_____

•◆•

❖ May ❖ 21

**RANDOMLY OPEN YOUR BIBLE
AND WRITE DOWN THE VERSE YOU SEE.**

20__: _____

_____

_____

_____

•◆•

20__: _____

_____

_____

_____

•◆•

20__: _____

_____

_____

_____

•◆•

 ❖ May ❖

WHAT ARE YOU WAITING ON GOD FOR?

20__: _____

_____

_____

_____

•◆•

20__: _____

_____

_____

_____

•◆•

20__: _____

_____

_____

_____

•◆•

IF YOU HAD $50 TO GIVE AWAY, WHAT WOULD YOU DO WITH IT?

20___: _____

_____

_____

_____

•◆•

20___: _____

_____

_____

_____

•◆•

20___: _____

_____

_____

_____

•◆•

 ❖ May ❖

WHO IS THE MOST CHALLENGING PERSON IN YOUR LIFE RIGHT NOW?

20__: _____

_____

_____

_____

• ◆ •

20__: _____

_____

_____

_____

• ◆ •

20__: _____

_____

_____

_____

• ◆ •

❖ May ❖

WHERE DID YOU SEE
GOD'S HAND IN NATURE TODAY?

20__: _____

_____

_____

_____

•◆•

20__: _____

_____

_____

_____

•◆•

20__: _____

_____

_____

_____

•◆•

❖ May ❖

WHAT RANDOM ACTS OF KINDNESS
HAVE YOU PERFORMED?

20__: _____

_____

_____

_____

• ◆ •

20__: _____

_____

_____

_____

• ◆ •

20__: _____

_____

_____

_____

• ◆ •

❖ May ❖ 27

WHO HAVE YOU THANKED TODAY?

20__: _____

_____

_____

_____

●◆●

20__: _____

_____

_____

_____

●◆●

20__: _____

_____

_____

_____

●◆●

❖ May ❖

WHO IS ON SPEED DIAL ON YOUR PHONE?

20__: _____

_____

_____

_____

• ◆ •

20__: _____

_____

_____

_____

• ◆ •

20__: _____

_____

_____

_____

• ◆ •

❖ May ❖

TOP THREE WEBSITES YOU VISIT.

20___: _____

_____

_____

_____

•◆•

20___: _____

_____

_____

_____

•◆•

20___: _____

_____

_____

_____

•◆•

❖ May ❖

SUREST ROAD TO DISCOURAGEMENT
IN YOUR LIFE.

20__: _____

_____

_____

_____

• ◆ •

20__: _____

_____

_____

_____

• ◆ •

20__: _____

_____

_____

_____

• ◆ •

ON A SCALE FROM 1-10, HOW HUMBLE WERE YOU TODAY?

20__: _____

_____

_____

_____

•◆•

20__: _____

_____

_____

_____

•◆•

20__: _____

_____

_____

_____

•◆•

1

❖ June ❖

WHAT ASPECT OF GOD'S CHARACTER HAS ENCOURAGED YOU THE MOST?

20__: _____

_____

_____

_____

•◆•

20__: _____

_____

_____

_____

•◆•

20__: _____

_____

_____

_____

•◆•

❖ June ❖

WHICH FRUIT OF THE SPIRIT IS MOST LACKING IN YOUR LIFE?

20___: _____

_____

_____

_____

•◆•

20___: _____

_____

_____

_____

•◆•

20___: _____

_____

_____

_____

•◆•

❖ June ❖

WHEN DID YOU LAST OPEN YOUR HOME TO STRANGERS?

20___: _____

_____

_____

_____

•◆•

20___: _____

_____

_____

_____

•◆•

20___: _____

_____

_____

_____

•◆•

❖ June ❖

WHAT BOOK OF THE BIBLE DO YOU WISH YOU UNDERSTOOD MORE?

20__: _____

_____

_____

_____

•◆•

20__: _____

_____

_____

_____

•◆•

20__: _____

_____

_____

_____

•◆•

❖ June ❖

THINK ABOUT A QUESTION THAT BAFFLES YOU ABOUT GOD.

20__: _____

_____

_____

_____

● ◆ ●

20__: _____

_____

_____

_____

● ◆ ●

20__: _____

_____

_____

_____

● ◆ ●

❖ June ❖

WHO DO YOU LONG TO BE RECONCILED WITH?

20__: _____

_____

_____

_____

•◆•

20__: _____

_____

_____

_____

•◆•

20__: _____

_____

_____

_____

•◆•

7

DESCRIBE YOUR PRESENT SELF IN THREE WORDS.

20___: _____

_____

_____

_____

•◆•

20___: _____

_____

_____

_____

•◆•

20___: _____

_____

_____

_____

•◆•

DESCRIBE WHO YOU WOULD LIKE TO BE IN THREE WORDS.

20__: _____

_____

_____

_____

• ◆ •

20__: _____

_____

_____

_____

• ◆ •

20__: _____

_____

_____

_____

• ◆ •

❖ June ❖

WHAT ARE THE TOP NEWS STORIES RIGHT NOW?

20___: _____

_____

_____

_____

• ◆ •

20___: _____

_____

_____

_____

• ◆ •

20___: _____

_____

_____

_____

• ◆ •

❖ June ❖ 10

LAST MIRACLE YOU WITNESSED.

20__: _____

_____

_____

_____

•◆•

20__: _____

_____

_____

_____

•◆•

20__: _____

_____

_____

_____

•◆•

11

❖ June ❖

WHAT HAS GOD TAUGHT YOU
THROUGH THE LAST DELAY YOU FACED?

20__: _____

_____

_____

_____

•◆•

20__: _____

_____

_____

_____

•◆•

20__: _____

_____

_____

_____

•◆•

❖ June ❖ 12

IF YOU COULD CHANGE ONE THING ABOUT YOURSELF, WHAT WOULD IT BE?

20___: _____

_____

_____

•◆•

20___: _____

_____

_____

•◆•

20___: _____

_____

_____

•◆•

13 ❖ June ❖

WHAT DO YOU DO TO RELAX?

20__: _____
_____
_____
_____

•◆•

20__: _____
_____
_____
_____

•◆•

20__: _____
_____
_____
_____

•◆•

❖ June ❖

14

WHAT KEEPS YOU UP AT NIGHT?

20__: _____

_____

_____

_____

• ◆ •

20__: _____

_____

_____

_____

• ◆ •

20__: _____

_____

_____

_____

• ◆ •

15

❖ June ❖

IF YOU COULD ASK JESUS A QUESTION IN PERSON RIGHT NOW, WHAT WOULD IT BE?

20__: _____

_____

_____

_____

•◆•

20__: _____

_____

_____

_____

•◆•

20__: _____

_____

_____

_____

•◆•

WHO IS YOUR HERO OF THE FAITH?

20__: _____

_____

_____

_____

• ◆ •

20__: _____

_____

_____

_____

• ◆ •

20__: _____

_____

_____

_____

• ◆ •

17

❖ June ❖

WHAT DO YOU ADMIRE MOST
ABOUT YOUR HERO OF THE FAITH?

20__: _____

_____

_____

_____

•◆•

20__: _____

_____

_____

_____

•◆•

20__: _____

_____

_____

_____

•◆•

❖ June ❖

18

WHAT IS ONE THING YOU WISH YOU'D ACCOMPLISHED THIS YEAR?

20__: _____

_____

_____

_____

•◆•

20__: _____

_____

_____

_____

•◆•

20__: _____

_____

_____

_____

•◆•

19

❖ June ❖

BEST GIFT YOU'VE EVER RECEIVED.

20__: _____
_____
_____
_____

•◆•

20__: _____
_____
_____
_____

•◆•

20__: _____
_____
_____
_____

•◆•

❖ June ❖

ON A SCALE FROM 1-10,
HOW JOYFUL WERE YOU TODAY?

20__: _____

_____

_____

_____

•◆•

20__: _____

_____

_____

_____

•◆•

20__: _____

_____

_____

_____

•◆•

21

❖ June ❖

**YOU ARE FEARFULLY AND WONDERFULLY MADE.
HOW DO YOU FEEL ABOUT THIS RIGHT NOW?**

20___: _____

_____

_____

_____

• ◆ •

20___: _____

_____

_____

_____

• ◆ •

20___: _____

_____

_____

_____

• ◆ •

❖ June ❖

WHO ARE YOU MOST
BURDENED FOR RIGHT NOW?

20___: _____

_____

_____

_____

• ◆ •

20___: _____

_____

_____

_____

• ◆ •

20___: _____

_____

_____

_____

• ◆ •

23 ❖ June ❖

**HOPE DEFERRED MAKES THE HEART SICK. IN
WHAT AREA IS YOUR HOPE BEING DEFERRED?**

20__: _____

_____

_____

_____

•◆•

20__: _____

_____

_____

_____

•◆•

20__: _____

_____

_____

_____

•◆•

❖ June ❖

THIS IS THE DAY THE LORD HAS MADE. DID TODAY FEEL LIKE THAT FOR YOU?

20__: _____

_____

_____

_____

•◆•

20__: _____

_____

_____

_____

•◆•

20__: _____

_____

_____

_____

•◆•

❖ June ❖

IF YOU HAD AN EXTRA HOUR IN THE DAY WHAT WOULD YOU DO WITH IT?

20__: _____

_____

_____

_____

•◆•

20__: _____

_____

_____

_____

•◆•

20__: _____

_____

_____

_____

•◆•

❖ June ❖

WHAT MAKES YOU FEEL SORRY FOR YOURSELF IN THIS SEASON OF LIFE?

20___: _____

_____

_____

_____

• ◆ •

20___: _____

_____

_____

_____

• ◆ •

20___: _____

_____

_____

_____

• ◆ •

27 ❖ June ❖

IF YOU COULD CHANGE ONE THING ABOUT YOURSELF, WHAT WOULD IT BE?

20___: _____

_____

_____

_____

•◆•

20___: _____

_____

_____

_____

•◆•

20___: _____

_____

_____

_____

•◆•

❖ June ❖

28

WHAT GIFT OF THE SPIRIT DO YOU WANT MORE OF?

20__: _____

_____

_____

_____

•◆•

20__: _____

_____

_____

_____

•◆•

20__: _____

_____

_____

_____

•◆•

❖ June ❖

WHAT TEMPTATION IS THE EASIEST ONE FOR YOU TO YIELD TO?

20___: _____

_____

_____

_____

•◆•

20___: _____

_____

_____

_____

•◆•

20___: _____

_____

_____

_____

•◆•

❖ June ❖ 30

WHICH SOCIAL JUSTICE ISSUE BURDENS YOU THE MOST RIGHT NOW?

20__: _____

_____

_____

_____

•◆•

20__: _____

_____

_____

_____

•◆•

20__: _____

_____

_____

_____

•◆•

1

❖ July ❖

WHEN WAS THE LAST TIME YOU HAD A REAL SENSE OF GOD'S PRESENCE IN YOUR LIFE?

20__: _____

_____

_____

_____

•◆•

20__: _____

_____

_____

_____

•◆•

20__: _____

_____

_____

_____

•◆•

❖ July ❖

WHAT ONE THING CAN'T YOU LIVE WITHOUT?

20___: _____

_____

_____

_____

•◆•

20___: _____

_____

_____

_____

•◆•

20___: _____

_____

_____

_____

•◆•

❖ July ❖

IN WHAT SPECIFIC WAYS HAS GOD PROVIDED FOR YOU THIS WEEK?

20__: _____

_____

_____

_____

•◆•

20__: _____

_____

_____

_____

•◆•

20__: _____

_____

_____

_____

•◆•

❖ July ❖

Where do you go most regularly to pray seriously?

20__: _____

_____

_____

_____

• ◆ •

20__: _____

_____

_____

_____

• ◆ •

20__: _____

_____

_____

_____

• ◆ •

❖ July ❖

LAST BIG DECISION YOU MADE WITHOUT PRAYING.

20__: _____

_____

_____

_____

•◆•

20__: _____

_____

_____

_____

•◆•

20__: _____

_____

_____

_____

•◆•

❖ July ❖

LAST BIG DECISION
YOU MADE AFTER SERIOUS PRAYER.

20__: _____

_____

_____

_____

•◆•

20__: _____

_____

_____

_____

•◆•

20__: _____

_____

_____

_____

•◆•

7

❖ July ❖

LIST ONE WAY GOD HAS BLOWN YOU AWAY RECENTLY.

20__: _____

_____

_____

_____

•◆•

20__: _____

_____

_____

_____

•◆•

20__: _____

_____

_____

_____

•◆•

❖ July ❖

IF GOD COULD HEAL YOU IMMEDIATELY IN ONE AREA, WHICH AREA WOULD YOU CHOOSE?

20__: _____

_____

_____

_____

•◆•

20__: _____

_____

_____

_____

•◆•

20__: _____

_____

_____

_____

•◆•

❖ July ❖

**ONE MEMORY THIS YEAR SO FAR
YOU WOULD LOVE TO REPLAY.**

20___: _____

_____

_____

_____

• ◆ •

20___: _____

_____

_____

_____

• ◆ •

20___: _____

_____

_____

_____

• ◆ •

❖ July ❖

ONE DAY THIS YEAR
YOU WISH YOU COULD FORGET.

20__: _____

_____

_____

_____

• ◆ •

20__: _____

_____

_____

_____

• ◆ •

20__: _____

_____

_____

_____

• ◆ •

11

❖ July ❖

WHAT IS ONE THING
YOU WISH PEOPLE KNEW ABOUT YOU?

20__: _____

_____

_____

_____

•◆•

20__: _____

_____

_____

_____

•◆•

20__: _____

_____

_____

_____

•◆•

❖ July ❖

WHEN WAS THE LAST TIME YOU FASTED ANYTHING?

20___: _____

_____

_____

_____

• ◆ •

20___: _____

_____

_____

_____

• ◆ •

20___: _____

_____

_____

_____

• ◆ •

13 ❖ July ❖

WHAT FEELS LIKE LOVE TO YOU?

20__: _____

_____

_____

_____

•◆•

20__: _____

_____

_____

_____

•◆•

20__: _____

_____

_____

_____

•◆•

❖ July ❖ 14

WHAT DO YOU WISH
YOUR PASTOR KNEW ABOUT YOU?

20__: _____

_____

_____

_____

•◆•

20__: _____

_____

_____

_____

•◆•

20__: _____

_____

_____

_____

•◆•

15 ❖ July ❖

How would your closest friends describe you?

20__: _____

_____

_____

_____

•◆•

20__: _____

_____

_____

_____

•◆•

20__: _____

_____

_____

_____

•◆•

❖ July ❖ 16

HOW WOULD A STRANGER DESCRIBE YOU?

20__: _____

_____

_____

_____

•◆•

20__: _____

_____

_____

_____

•◆•

20__: _____

_____

_____

_____

•◆•

17

❖ July ❖

ON A SCALE FROM 1-10, HOW ANGRY WERE YOU TODAY?

20__: _____

_____

_____

_____

•◆•

20__: _____

_____

_____

_____

•◆•

20__: _____

_____

_____

_____

•◆•

❖ July ❖ 18

WHAT MAKES YOU IMPATIENT?

20__: _____
_____
_____
_____

•◆•

20__: _____
_____
_____
_____

•◆•

20__: _____
_____
_____
_____

•◆•

19

❖ July ❖

WHAT BRINGS DISCOURAGEMENT IN YOUR LIFE?

20__: _____

_____

_____

_____

•◆•

20__: _____

_____

_____

_____

•◆•

20__: _____

_____

_____

_____

•◆•

❖ July ❖

IF GOD COULD REVIVE A DEAD DREAM, WHICH WOULD YOU ASK HIM TO REVIVE?

20__: _____

_____

_____

_____

•◆•

20__: _____

_____

_____

_____

•◆•

20__: _____

_____

_____

_____

•◆•

21

❖ July ❖

WHAT SITUATION THIS YEAR STARTED OUT BADLY, BUT GOD WORKED OUT FOR GOOD?

20__: _____

_____

_____

_____

•◆•

20__: _____

_____

_____

_____

•◆•

20__: _____

_____

_____

_____

•◆•

YOU'RE GIVEN ONE WEEK OFF ON SHORT NOTICE. WHAT WOULD YOU DO WITH IT?

20___: _____

_____

_____

_____

• ◆ •

20___: _____

_____

_____

_____

• ◆ •

20___: _____

_____

_____

_____

• ◆ •

23

❖ July ❖

WHAT ARE SOME THINGS THAT YOU PRACTICE NOW THAT WILL ONLY MAKE SENSE IN ETERNITY?

20__: _____

_____

_____

_____

•◆•

20__: _____

_____

_____

_____

•◆•

20__: _____

_____

_____

_____

•◆•

IF JESUS WERE TO RETURN TOMORROW, HOW WOULD YOU SPEND TODAY?

20__: _____

_____

_____

_____

•◆•

20__: _____

_____

_____

_____

•◆•

20__: _____

_____

_____

_____

•◆•

25

❖ July ❖

WHAT BRINGS TEARS TO YOUR EYES?

20__: _____

_____

_____

_____

•◆•

20__: _____

_____

_____

_____

•◆•

20__: _____

_____

_____

_____

•◆•

❖ July ❖

WHEN WAS THE LAST TIME
SOMEONE TOLD YOU "I LOVE YOU"?

20__: _____

_____

_____

_____

•◆•

20__: _____

_____

_____

_____

•◆•

20__: _____

_____

_____

_____

•◆•

27

❖ July ❖

WHEN WAS THE LAST TIME
SOMEONE TOLD YOU "I TOLD YOU SO"?

20__: _____

_____

_____

_____

• ◆ •

20__: _____

_____

_____

_____

• ◆ •

20__: _____

_____

_____

_____

• ◆ •

❖ July ❖

I FEEL CLOSEST TO GOD WHEN I
_____.

20__: _____

_____

_____

_____

•◆•

20__: _____

_____

_____

_____

•◆•

20__: _____

_____

_____

_____

•◆•

 ❖ July ❖

I FEEL MOST GUILTY WHEN **I** _____.

20__: _____

_____

_____

_____

•◆•

20__: _____

_____

_____

_____

•◆•

20__: _____

_____

_____

_____

•◆•

❖ July ❖ 30

WHAT IS YOUR BEST MEMORY OF THIS YEAR?

20__: _____

_____

_____

_____

• ◆ •

20__: _____

_____

_____

_____

• ◆ •

20__: _____

_____

_____

_____

• ◆ •

31

❖ July ❖

IN WHAT WAYS DID YOU
MAKE THE MOST OF TODAY?

20___: _____

_____

_____

_____

• ◆ •

20___: _____

_____

_____

_____

• ◆ •

20___: _____

_____

_____

_____

• ◆ •

IF SOMEONE GAVE YOU $1 MILLION HOW WOULD YOU SPEND IT?

20__: _____

_____

_____

_____

•◆•

20__: _____

_____

_____

_____

•◆•

20__: _____

_____

_____

_____

•◆•

❖ August ❖

WHERE DID YOU WASTE VALUABLE TIME TODAY?

20__: _____

_____

_____

_____

•◆•

20__: _____

_____

_____

_____

•◆•

20__: _____

_____

_____

_____

•◆•

ARE THERE AREAS OF IMBALANCE IN YOUR LIFE RIGHT NOW?

20__: _____

_____

_____

_____

• ◆ •

20__: _____

_____

_____

_____

• ◆ •

20__: _____

_____

_____

_____

• ◆ •

❖ August ❖

WHEN WAS THE LAST TIME YOU COMPLIMENTED SOMEONE AND MEANT IT?

20__: _____

_____

_____

_____

•◆•

20__: _____

_____

_____

_____

•◆•

20__: _____

_____

_____

_____

•◆•

RATE THE NOISE LEVEL IN YOUR LIFE AND ONE
OR TWO PRACTICAL WAYS TO TURN IT DOWN.

20___: _____

_____

_____

_____

•◆•

20___: _____

_____

_____

_____

•◆•

20___: _____

_____

_____

_____

•◆•

❖ **August** ❖

WHAT IS THE ONE THING YOU WOULD DO IF YOU WEREN'T AFRAID?

20___: _____

_____

_____

_____

•◆•

20___: _____

_____

_____

_____

•◆•

20___: _____

_____

_____

_____

•◆•

❖ August ❖

**HOW DID YOU REACT
TO INCONVENIENCES TODAY?**

20___: _____

_____

_____

_____

•◆•

20___: _____

_____

_____

_____

•◆•

20___: _____

_____

_____

_____

•◆•

❖ August ❖

WHAT ARE YOU WAITING ON THE LORD FOR?

20__: _____

_____

_____

_____

•◆•

20__: _____

_____

_____

_____

•◆•

20__: _____

_____

_____

_____

•◆•

❖ August ❖

WHERE DID YOU TURN TO FIND JOY AND SATISFACTION TODAY?

20___: _____

_____

_____

_____

•◆•

20___: _____

_____

_____

_____

•◆•

20___: _____

_____

_____

_____

•◆•

10 ❖ August ❖

WHAT MEMORY BRINGS YOU JOY RIGHT NOW?

20__: _____

_____

_____

_____

•◆•

20__: _____

_____

_____

_____

•◆•

20__: _____

_____

_____

_____

•◆•

WHAT RELATIONSHIP IN YOUR LIFE LEAVES YOU FEELING REGRET?

20__: _____

_____

_____

_____

•◆•

20__: _____

_____

_____

_____

•◆•

20__: _____

_____

_____

_____

•◆•

12 ❖ August ❖

WHAT'S YOUR FAVORITE QUOTE?

20__: _____

_____

_____

_____

• ◆ •

20__: _____

_____

_____

_____

• ◆ •

20__: _____

_____

_____

_____

• ◆ •

❖ August ❖ 13

WHAT MADE YOU MAD TODAY?

20__: _____

_____

_____

_____

• ◆ •

20__: _____

_____

_____

_____

• ◆ •

20__: _____

_____

_____

_____

• ◆ •

14 ❖ August ❖

WHAT IS STEALING YOUR PEACE?

20__: _____

_____

_____

_____

•❖•

20__: _____

_____

_____

_____

•❖•

20__: _____

_____

_____

_____

•❖•

❖ August ❖ 15

WHEN WAS THE LAST TIME
YOU FELT YOUR HEART BREAK?

20___: _____

_____

_____

_____

• ◆ •

20___: _____

_____

_____

_____

• ◆ •

20___: _____

_____

_____

_____

• ◆ •

16 ❖ August ❖

WHEN WAS THE LAST TIME YOU FELT YOU REALLY CONNECTED WITH CHRIST?

20__: _____

_____

_____

_____

• ◆ •

20__: _____

_____

_____

_____

• ◆ •

20__: _____

_____

_____

_____

• ◆ •

IN WHAT WAY DID YOU PRACTICE THE SABBATH THIS WEEK?

20___: _____

_____

_____

_____

•◆•

20___: _____

_____

_____

_____

•◆•

20___: _____

_____

_____

_____

•◆•

18 ❖ August ❖

WHAT ONE PRACTICE/DISCIPLINE DO YOU WISH YOU COULD INTEGRATE IN YOUR LIFE?

20__: _____

_____

_____

_____

•◆•

20__: _____

_____

_____

_____

•◆•

20__: _____

_____

_____

_____

•◆•

❖ August ❖ 19

WHAT DID YOU FIX YOUR EYES ON TODAY?

20___: _____

_____

_____

_____

• ◆ •

20___: _____

_____

_____

_____

• ◆ •

20___: _____

_____

_____

_____

• ◆ •

 ❖ August ❖

HOW DID YOU MAKE THE MOST
OF YOUR WAITING TODAY?

20__: _____

_____

_____

_____

•◆•

20__: _____

_____

_____

_____

•◆•

20__: _____

_____

_____

_____

•◆•

❖ August ❖ 21

WHAT'S ON YOUR TODAY LIST RIGHT NOW?

20___: _____

_____

_____

_____

•◆•

20___: _____

_____

_____

_____

•◆•

20___: _____

_____

_____

_____

•◆•

 ❖ August ❖

WHAT DO YOU WISH YOU COULD
PASS ON TO THE NEXT GENERATION?

20__: _____

_____

_____

_____

•◆•

20__: _____

_____

_____

_____

•◆•

20__: _____

_____

_____

_____

•◆•

❖ August ❖

WHAT NEEDS TWEAKING IN YOUR HOME RIGHT NOW?

20__: _____

_____

_____

_____

•◆•

20__: _____

_____

_____

_____

•◆•

20__: _____

_____

_____

_____

•◆•

 ❖ August ❖

WHEN WAS THE LAST TIME YOU MADE YOURSELF VULNERABLE WITH ANOTHER PERSON?

20___: _____

_____

_____

_____

•◆•

20___: _____

_____

_____

_____

•◆•

20___: _____

_____

_____

_____

•◆•

WHAT MAKES YOU FEEL ASHAMED RIGHT NOW?

20__: _____
_____
_____
_____

• ◆ •

20__: _____
_____
_____
_____

• ◆ •

20__: _____
_____
_____
_____

• ◆ •

26 ❖ August ❖

IF SOMEONE COULD SEE THROUGH YOUR THOUGHTS, WHAT WOULD THEY FIND?

20__: _____

_____

_____

_____

•◆•

20__: _____

_____

_____

_____

•◆•

20__: _____

_____

_____

_____

•◆•

❖ August ❖ 27

WHAT IS YOUR LAST BIG SUCCESS?

20__: _____

_____

_____

_____

•◆•

20__: _____

_____

_____

_____

•◆•

20__: _____

_____

_____

_____

•◆•

❖ August ❖

WHAT IS YOUR LAST BIG FAILURE?

20__: _____

_____

_____

_____

•◆•

20__: _____

_____

_____

_____

•◆•

20__: _____

_____

_____

_____

•◆•

❖ August ❖

IF YOU HAD COURAGE TO MAKE THAT ONE BIG DECISION, WHAT WOULD IT BE?

20___: _____

_____

_____

_____

• ◆ •

20___: _____

_____

_____

_____

• ◆ •

20___: _____

_____

_____

_____

• ◆ •

30 ❖ August ❖

WHAT'S YOUR IDEA OF THE PROMISED LAND?

20__: _____

_____

_____

_____

•◆•

20__: _____

_____

_____

_____

•◆•

20__: _____

_____

_____

_____

•◆•

❖ August ❖ 31

WHAT ARE YOU LOOKING FORWARD TO THE MOST IN HEAVEN?

20__: _____

_____

_____

_____

●◆●

20__: _____

_____

_____

_____

●◆●

20__: _____

_____

_____

_____

●◆●

1

❖ **September** ❖

IF YOU COULD ASK YOUR HERO
ONE QUESTION IT WOULD BE:

20__: _____

_____

_____

_____

•◆•

20__: _____

_____

_____

_____

•◆•

20__: _____

_____

_____

_____

•◆•

❖ September ❖

ON A SCALE FROM 1–10, HOW WOULD YOU RATE YOUR KINDNESS TO OTHERS?

20__: _____

_____

_____

_____

•◆•

20__: _____

_____

_____

_____

•◆•

20__: _____

_____

_____

_____

•◆•

3

❖ **September** ❖

HOW DID YOU SHOW COMPASSION
TO SOMEONE TODAY?

20___: _____

_____

_____

_____

•◆•

20___: _____

_____

_____

_____

•◆•

20___: _____

_____

_____

_____

•◆•

❖ September ❖

**IF SOMEONE CLOSE TO YOU WAS ASKED
HOW CHRISTLIKE YOU ACTED TODAY,
HE/SHE WOULD SAY:**

20__: _____

_____

_____

_____

•◆•

20__: _____

_____

_____

_____

•◆•

20__: _____

_____

_____

_____

•◆•

❖ September ❖

WHAT MIRACLE DID YOU WITNESS TODAY?

20__: _____

_____

_____

_____

•◆•

20__: _____

_____

_____

_____

•◆•

20__: _____

_____

_____

_____

•◆•

❖ September ❖

**IF ALL YOUR THOUGHTS WERE ON
PUBLIC DISPLAY HOW WOULD IT MAKE YOU FEEL?**

20__: _____

_____

_____

_____

•◆•

20__: _____

_____

_____

_____

•◆•

20__: _____

_____

_____

_____

•◆•

7

❖ September ❖

How's your relationship with your local church?

20___: _____

_____

_____

_____

•◆•

20___: _____

_____

_____

_____

•◆•

20___: _____

_____

_____

_____

•◆•

WHAT IS FRUSTRATING YOU ABOUT YOUR SMALL GROUP OR CHRISTIAN COMMUNITY?

20__: _____

_____

_____

_____

•◆•

20__: _____

_____

_____

_____

•◆•

20__: _____

_____

_____

_____

•◆•

❖ September ❖

**IF YOU HAD THIS ONE THING _____
YOU WOULD BE HAPPY.**

20__: _____

_____

_____

_____

•◆•

20__: _____

_____

_____

_____

•◆•

20__: _____

_____

_____

_____

•◆•

❖ September ❖ 10

HOW DID GOD SHOW YOU HIS LONGSUFFERING TODAY?

20___: _____

_____

_____

_____

•◆•

20___: _____

_____

_____

_____

•◆•

20___: _____

_____

_____

_____

•◆•

11 ❖ September ❖

WHAT IS GOD TEACHING YOU THROUGH YOUR PRESENT CIRCUMSTANCES?

20__: _____

_____

_____

_____

•◆•

20__: _____

_____

_____

_____

•◆•

20__: _____

_____

_____

_____

•◆•

❖ September ❖ 12

WHAT BOOK COULD YOU READ OVER AND OVER AGAIN?

20__: _____

_____

_____

_____

•◆•

20__: _____

_____

_____

_____

•◆•

20__: _____

_____

_____

_____

•◆•

13 ❖ September ❖

**IF YOU COULD LEARN TO MAKE ONE THING,
WHAT WOULD IT BE?**

20__: _____

_____

_____

_____

• ◆ •

20__: _____

_____

_____

_____

• ◆ •

20__: _____

_____

_____

_____

• ◆ •

RATE THE STRENGTH OF YOUR CHRISTIAN COMMUNITY RIGHT NOW?

20__: _____

_____

_____

_____

•◆•

20__: _____

_____

_____

_____

•◆•

20__: _____

_____

_____

_____

•◆•

15 ❖ September ❖

WHEN WAS THE LAST TIME
YOU LED SOMEONE TO JESUS?

20__: _____

_____

_____

_____

• ◆ •

20__: _____

_____

_____

_____

• ◆ •

20__: _____

_____

_____

_____

• ◆ •

WHO ARE YOU DISCIPLING RIGHT NOW?

20__: _____

_____

_____

_____

• ◆ •

20__: _____

_____

_____

_____

• ◆ •

20__: _____

_____

_____

_____

• ◆ •

17 ❖ September ❖

IN WHAT WAYS ARE YOU BEING PERSECUTED
FOR YOUR FAITH RIGHT NOW?

20__: _____

_____

_____

_____

•◆•

20__: _____

_____

_____

_____

•◆•

20__: _____

_____

_____

_____

•◆•

❖ September ❖ 18

WHAT'S THE NEXT STEP OF FAITH GOD IS ASKING YOU TO TAKE?

20__: _____

_____

_____

_____

• ◆ •

20__: _____

_____

_____

_____

• ◆ •

20__: _____

_____

_____

_____

• ◆ •

19 ❖ September ❖

HOW DID YOU SHOW PATIENCE TODAY?

20__: _____

_____

_____

_____

•◆•

20__: _____

_____

_____

_____

•◆•

20__: _____

_____

_____

_____

•◆•

❖ September ❖

WHEN WAS THE LAST TIME YOU SAID "NO" TO SIN?

20__: _____

_____

_____

_____

•◆•

20__: _____

_____

_____

_____

•◆•

20__: _____

_____

_____

_____

•◆•

21

❖ September ❖

WHEN WAS THE LAST TIME YOU TALKED TO A COMPLETE STRANGER ABOUT JESUS?

20__: _____

_____

_____

_____

• ◆ •

20__: _____

_____

_____

_____

• ◆ •

20__: _____

_____

_____

_____

• ◆ •

❖ September ❖

WORDS TO A LOVED ONE YOU WISH YOU COULD TAKE BACK THIS WEEK.

20__: _____
_____
_____
_____

•◆•

20__: _____
_____
_____
_____

•◆•

20__: _____
_____
_____
_____

•◆•

23 ❖ September ❖

WORDS YOU SAID TO SOMEONE THAT SOWED LIFE INTO THEM.

20__: _____

_____

_____

_____

•◆•

20__: _____

_____

_____

_____

•◆•

20__: _____

_____

_____

_____

•◆•

❖ September ❖

LAST PERSON YOU REALLY HUGGED.

20__: _____

_____

_____

_____

•◆•

20__: _____

_____

_____

_____

•◆•

20__: _____

_____

_____

_____

•◆•

25 ❖ September ❖

DESCRIBE YOUR SEASON OF LIFE RIGHT NOW.

20__: _____

_____

_____

_____

•◆•

20__: _____

_____

_____

_____

•◆•

20__: _____

_____

_____

_____

•◆•

❖ September ❖

JOT DOWN YOUR PRESENT READING LIST.

20__: _____

_____

_____

_____

• ◆ •

20__: _____

_____

_____

_____

• ◆ •

20__: _____

_____

_____

_____

• ◆ •

27 ❖ September ❖

**BIBLE STORY YOU FEEL
YOU'RE LIVING THROUGH RIGHT NOW.**

20__: _____

_____

_____

_____

•◆•

20__: _____

_____

_____

_____

•◆•

20__: _____

_____

_____

_____

•◆•

❖ September ❖

WHAT DO YOU DREAM ABOUT THESE DAYS?

20___: _____

_____

_____

_____

• ◆ •

20___: _____

_____

_____

_____

• ◆ •

20___: _____

_____

_____

_____

• ◆ •

 ❖ September ❖

WHAT HAS YOU DISAPPOINTED RIGHT NOW?

20__: _____

_____

_____

_____

•◆•

20__: _____

_____

_____

_____

•◆•

20__: _____

_____

_____

_____

•◆•

WHAT STILL GIVES YOU HOPE IN YOUR PRESENT DISAPPOINTMENT?

20__: _____

_____

_____

_____

●◆●

20__: _____

_____

_____

_____

●◆●

20__: _____

_____

_____

_____

●◆●

1

❖ October ❖

SOMEONE YOU RESOLVE TO SEND A HANDWRITTEN NOTE OF ENCOURAGEMENT TO THIS WEEK.

20___: _____

_____

_____

_____

•◆•

20___: _____

_____

_____

_____

•◆•

20___: _____

_____

_____

_____

•◆•

❖ October ❖

**YOUR GREATEST REGRET THIS YEAR
SO FAR IN THE AREA OF GIVING.**

20___: _____
_____
_____
_____

•◆•

20___: _____
_____
_____
_____

•◆•

20___: _____
_____
_____
_____

•◆•

❖ October ❖

DID YOU MAKE IT TO CHURCH THIS WEEK?

20__: _____

_____

_____

_____

• ◆ •

20__: _____

_____

_____

_____

• ◆ •

20__: _____

_____

_____

_____

• ◆ •

❖ October ❖

4

VERSE OF THE WEEK FOR YOU.

20__: _____
_____
_____
_____

• ◆ •

20__: _____
_____
_____
_____

• ◆ •

20__: _____
_____
_____
_____

• ◆ •

❖ **October** ❖

FIVE THINGS YOU PRAISE THE LORD FOR.

20__: _____

_____

_____

_____

•◆•

20__: _____

_____

_____

_____

•◆•

20__: _____

_____

_____

_____

•◆•

❖ October ❖

SUMMARIZE THIS YEAR SO FAR IN A SENTENCE.

20__: _____

_____

_____

_____

• ◆ •

20__: _____

_____

_____

_____

• ◆ •

20__: _____

_____

_____

_____

• ◆ •

7 ❖ October ❖

**WHAT YOU WISH YOUR
CLOSEST FRIENDS KNEW ABOUT YOU.**

20___: _____

_____

_____

_____

•◆•

20___: _____

_____

_____

•◆•

20___: _____

_____

_____

_____

•◆•

❖ October ❖

**IS THERE ANYTHING YOU ARE DOING
IN SECRET RIGHT NOW YOU HOPE
NO ONE EVER FINDS OUT ABOUT?**

20__: _____

_____

_____

_____

•◆•

20__: _____

_____

_____

_____

•◆•

20__: _____

_____

_____

_____

•◆•

❖ October ❖

IF YOUR LIFE WERE A MOVIE, WHAT GENRE WOULD IT BE IN?

20__: _____

_____

_____

_____

•◆•

20__: _____

_____

_____

_____

•◆•

20__: _____

_____

_____

_____

•◆•

**IF YOU WERE ASKED TO PREACH A SERMON,
WHAT WOULD ITS TITLE BE?**

20__: _____

_____

_____

_____

•◆•

20__: _____

_____

_____

_____

•◆•

20__: _____

_____

_____

_____

•◆•

11

❖ October ❖

HOW HAS GOD MET YOUR
MATERIAL NEEDS THIS WEEK?

20__: _____

_____

_____

_____

•◆•

20__: _____

_____

_____

_____

•◆•

20__: _____

_____

_____

_____

•◆•

❖ October ❖ 12

WHO HAS GOD USED TO STRENGTHEN YOUR SPIRIT THIS WEEK?

20__: _____

_____

_____

_____

•◆•

20__: _____

_____

_____

_____

•◆•

20__: _____

_____

_____

_____

•◆•

13 ❖ October ❖

WHAT PROMISE OF GOD ARE YOU HANGING ON TO RIGHT NOW?

20__: _____

_____

_____

_____

•◆•

20__: _____

_____

_____

_____

•◆•

20__: _____

_____

_____

_____

•◆•

❖ October ❖ 14

ON A SCALE OF 1-10, HOW WORRIED ARE YOU ABOUT YOUR FUTURE?

20__: _____

_____

_____

_____

• ◆ •

20__: _____

_____

_____

_____

• ◆ •

20__: _____

_____

_____

_____

• ◆ •

15 ❖ October ❖

IN THIS SEASON OF YOUR LIFE, ARE YOU AN OVERCOMER OR DEFEATED?

20__: _____

_____

_____

_____

• ◆ •

20__: _____

_____

_____

_____

• ◆ •

20__: _____

_____

_____

_____

• ◆ •

WHAT SPECIFIC CHANGES
ARE YOU GOING THROUGH RIGHT NOW?

20___: _____

_____

_____

_____

•◆•

20___: _____

_____

_____

_____

•◆•

20___: _____

_____

_____

_____

•◆•

17 ❖ October ❖

YOUR CLOSEST RELATIONSHIPS: BURDEN TO BEAR OR THERE WHEN YOU NEED THEM?

20__: _____

_____

_____

_____

• ◆ •

20__: _____

_____

_____

_____

• ◆ •

20__: _____

_____

_____

_____

• ◆ •

IF YOU COULD KEEP JUST ONE PAGE OF YOUR BIBLE, WHICH WOULD YOU CHOOSE?

20__: _____

_____

_____

_____

•◆•

20__: _____

_____

_____

_____

•◆•

20__: _____

_____

_____

_____

•◆•

19 ❖ October ❖

WHAT ASPECT OF GOD'S CHARACTER COULD YOU SPEND HOURS THINKING AND TALKING ABOUT?

20___: _____

_____

_____

_____

•◆•

20___: _____

_____

_____

_____

•◆•

20___: _____

_____

_____

_____

•◆•

❖ October ❖

HOW HAS GOD SURPRISED YOU THIS YEAR SO FAR?

20___: _____

_____

_____

_____

•◆•

20___: _____

_____

_____

_____

•◆•

20___: _____

_____

_____

_____

•◆•

21 ❖ October ❖

WHEN WAS THE LAST TIME YOU GAVE UNTIL IT HURT?

20__: _____

_____

_____

_____

•◆•

20__: _____

_____

_____

_____

•◆•

20__: _____

_____

_____

_____

•◆•

❖ October ❖

HOW DID YOU DIE TO YOURSELF TODAY?

20__: _____
_____
_____
_____

•◆•

20__: _____
_____
_____
_____

•◆•

20__: _____
_____
_____
_____

•◆•

23 ❖ October ❖

A LEADERSHIP QUALITY YOU ADMIRE AND WILL RESOLVE TO WORK ON IN YOUR LIFE NEXT.

20___: _____

_____

_____

_____

•◆•

20___: _____

_____

_____

_____

•◆•

20___: _____

_____

_____

_____

•◆•

❖ October ❖

WHAT ARE YOU ADDICTED TO?

20__: _____

_____

_____

_____

•◆•

20__: _____

_____

_____

_____

•◆•

20__: _____

_____

_____

_____

•◆•

 ❖ October ❖

HOW DOES YOUR ADDICTION BRING GLORY TO GOD?

20__: _____
_____
_____
_____

•◆•

20__: _____
_____
_____
_____

•◆•

20__: _____
_____
_____
_____

•◆•

❖ October ❖

WHERE WERE YOU TEMPTED TO CUT CORNERS TODAY?

20__: _____

_____

_____

_____

•◆•

20__: _____

_____

_____

_____

•◆•

20__: _____

_____

_____

_____

•◆•

27 ❖ October ❖

HOW MUCH TIME DID YOU SPEND SITTING STILL BEFORE THE LORD TODAY?

20__: _____

_____

_____

_____

•◆•

20__: _____

_____

_____

_____

•◆•

20__: _____

_____

_____

_____

•◆•

❖ October ❖

WHAT IS GOD ASKING YOU TO DO THAT YOU'RE HARD TIME OBEYING?

20__: _____

_____

_____

_____

• ◆ •

20__: _____

_____

_____

_____

• ◆ •

20__: _____

_____

_____

_____

• ◆ •

❖ October ❖

WHAT DO YOU VALUE THE MOST IN YOUR LIFE?

20__: _____

_____

_____

_____

• ◆ •

20__: _____

_____

_____

_____

• ◆ •

20__: _____

_____

_____

_____

• ◆ •

❖ October ❖

IF YOU COULD HAVE ONE SUPER POWER, WHAT WOULD YOU PICK?

20__: _____

_____

_____

_____

•◆•

20__: _____

_____

_____

_____

•◆•

20__: _____

_____

_____

_____

•◆•

31 ❖ October ❖

IS THERE A FRIENDSHIP IN YOUR LIFE RIGHT NOW THAT IS BRINGING YOU DOWN?

20__: _____

_____

_____

_____

• ◆ •

20__: _____

_____

_____

_____

• ◆ •

20__: _____

_____

_____

_____

• ◆ •

❖ November ❖

1

WHO OF YOUR FRIENDS SHOULD YOU SPEND MORE TIME WITH IN ORDER TO GET STRONGER?

20__: _____

_____

_____

_____

• ◆ •

20__: _____

_____

_____

_____

• ◆ •

20__: _____

_____

_____

_____

• ◆ •

❖ November ❖

DID YOU ASK GOD ABOUT
THE LAST BIG PURCHASE YOU MADE?

20__: _____

_____

_____

_____

•◆•

20__: _____

_____

_____

_____

•◆•

20__: _____

_____

_____

_____

•◆•

WHEN WAS THE LAST TIME YOU ASKED GOD FOR WISDOM?

20___: _____

_____

_____

_____

•◆•

20___: _____

_____

_____

_____

•◆•

20___: _____

_____

_____

_____

•◆•

❖ November ❖

WHEN WAS THE LAST TIME YOU HAD A REAL CONVERSATION WITH YOUR NEIGHBOR?

20___: _____

_____

_____

_____

• ◆ •

20___: _____

_____

_____

_____

• ◆ •

20___: _____

_____

_____

_____

• ◆ •

❖ November ❖

HOW MANY TIMES THIS MONTH HAVE YOU PRACTICED TRUE HOSPITALITY IN YOUR HOME?

20__: _____

_____

_____

_____

●◆●

20__: _____

_____

_____

_____

●◆●

20__: _____

_____

_____

_____

●◆●

❖ November ❖

WHEN WAS THE LAST TIME YOU GAVE UP YOUR OWN COMFORT FOR THE SAKE OF SOMEONE ELSE?

20__: _____

_____

_____

_____

•◆•

20__: _____

_____

_____

_____

•◆•

20__: _____

_____

_____

_____

•◆•

HOW DID YOU LOVE YOUR ENEMIES THIS WEEK?

20___: _____

_____

_____

_____

• ◆ •

20___: _____

_____

_____

_____

• ◆ •

20___: _____

_____

_____

_____

• ◆ •

HOW LONG BEFORE YOU STOPPED
AND TALKED TO THE LORD TODAY?

20__: _____

_____

_____

_____

• ◆ •

20__: _____

_____

_____

_____

• ◆ •

20__: _____

_____

_____

_____

• ◆ •

❖ November ❖

WHAT IS ONE MISTAKE
YOU CAN FIX FROM YESTERDAY?

20__: _____

_____

_____

_____

• ◆ •

20__: _____

_____

_____

_____

• ◆ •

20__: _____

_____

_____

_____

• ◆ •

10 ❖ November ❖

WHAT ARE YOU CRAVING
IN YOUR RELATIONSHIP WITH GOD?

20__: _____

_____

_____

_____

●◆●

20__: _____

_____

_____

_____

●◆●

20__: _____

_____

_____

_____

●◆●

WHAT SIN ARE YOU STILL HIDING IN YOUR HEART?

20__: _____

_____

_____

_____

•◆•

20__: _____

_____

_____

_____

•◆•

20__: _____

_____

_____

_____

•◆•

12 ❖ November ❖

WHAT'S YOUR RESOLUTION
FOR THE COMING WEEK?

20__: _____

_____

_____

_____

• ◆ •

20__: _____

_____

_____

_____

• ◆ •

20__: _____

_____

_____

_____

• ◆ •

❖ November ❖ 13

WHEN WAS THE LAST TIME YOU WERE PERSECUTED?

20__: _____

_____

_____

_____

•◆•

20__: _____

_____

_____

_____

•◆•

20__: _____

_____

_____

_____

•◆•

14 ❖ November ❖

WHAT'S YOUR LIFE VERSE?

20__: _____

_____

_____

_____

•◆•

20__: _____

_____

_____

_____

•◆•

20__: _____

_____

_____

_____

•◆•

❖ November ❖ 15

HOW DID YOU IGNORE
THE HOLY SPIRIT'S PROMPTING TODAY?

20__: _____

_____

_____

_____

• ◆ •

20__: _____

_____

_____

_____

• ◆ •

20__: _____

_____

_____

_____

• ◆ •

16 ❖ November ❖

IF SOMEONE WAS WATCHING A VIDEO
OF YOUR LIFE, WHAT WOULD THEY SEE?

20___: _____

_____

_____

_____

•◆•

20___: _____

_____

_____

_____

•◆•

20___: _____

_____

_____

_____

•◆•

❖ November ❖ 17

IF YOU COULD SERVE IN ANY AREA IN YOUR CHURCH, WHERE WOULD YOU SERVE?

20__: _____

_____

_____

_____

•◆•

20__: _____

_____

_____

_____

•◆•

20__: _____

_____

_____

_____

•◆•

18 ❖ November ❖

WHEN WAS THE LAST TIME YOU SAID "YES" TO GOD?

20__: _____

_____

_____

_____

•◆•

20__: _____

_____

_____

_____

•◆•

20__: _____

_____

_____

_____

•◆•

❖ November ❖ 19

MOST ANNOYING HABIT YOU HAVE.

20__: _____
_____
_____
_____

• ◆ •

20__: _____
_____
_____
_____

• ◆ •

20__: _____
_____
_____
_____

• ◆ •

 **❖ November ❖**

20

MOST EDIFYING HABIT YOU HAVE.

20___: _____

_____

_____

_____

•◆•

20___: _____

_____

_____

_____

•◆•

20___: _____

_____

_____

_____

•◆•

❖ November ❖ 21

THINK BACK TO THE LAST ONE GOD SPOKE TO YOU ABOUT. WHAT DID HE SAY?

20__: _____

_____

_____

_____

•◆•

20__: _____

_____

_____

_____

•◆•

20__: _____

_____

_____

_____

•◆•

❖ November ❖

HOW DID YOU RESPOND
THE LAST TIME GOD SPOKE TO YOU?

20__: _____

_____

_____

_____

• ◆ •

20__: _____

_____

_____

_____

• ◆ •

20__: _____

_____

_____

_____

• ◆ •

❖ November ❖ 23

WHEN WAS THE LAST TIME YOU SAW FRUIT OF YOUR OBEDIENCE TO GOD?

20__: _____

_____

_____

_____

• ◆ •

20__: _____

_____

_____

• ◆ •

20__: _____

_____

_____

_____

• ◆ •

24 ❖ November ❖

WHAT DID YOU DO TO REST UP TODAY?

20__: _____

_____

_____

_____

•◆•

20__: _____

_____

_____

_____

•◆•

20__: _____

_____

_____

_____

•◆•

❖ November ❖ 25

WHAT VERSE OR PASSAGE OF SCRIPTURE STUCK OUT TO YOU THIS WEEK?

20___: _____

_____

_____

_____

• ◆ •

20___: _____

_____

_____

_____

• ◆ •

20___: _____

_____

_____

_____

• ◆ •

 ❖ November ❖

TOP OF YOUR PRAYER LIST THIS WEEK.

20__: _____

_____

_____

_____

•◆•

20__: _____

_____

_____

_____

•◆•

20__: _____

_____

_____

_____

•◆•

HOW DID GOD SHOW HIMSELF FAITHFUL TO YOU TODAY?

20__: _____

_____

_____

_____

•◆•

20__: _____

_____

_____

_____

•◆•

20__: _____

_____

_____

_____

•◆•

 **❖ November ❖**

UNEXPECTED BLESSING TODAY.

20__: _____

_____

_____

_____

• ◆ •

20__: _____

_____

_____

_____

• ◆ •

20__: _____

_____

_____

_____

• ◆ •

❖ November ❖

LAST WILDERNESS SEASON BROUGHT THIS OUT IN YOU:

20___: _____

_____

_____

_____

• ◆ •

20___: _____

_____

_____

_____

• ◆ •

20___: _____

_____

_____

_____

• ◆ •

 **❖ November ❖**

LAST STRANGER
YOU HAD A CONVERSATION WITH.

20__: _____

_____

_____

_____

•◆•

20__: _____

_____

_____

_____

•◆•

20__: _____

_____

_____

_____

•◆•

❖ December ❖

1

**WHO COULD YOU GIVE AN
ANONYMOUS GIFT TO THIS WEEK?**

20___: _____

_____

_____

_____

•◆•

20___: _____

_____

_____

_____

•◆•

20___: _____

_____

_____

_____

•◆•

❖ December ❖

WHEN WAS THE LAST TIME YOU NOTICED SOMETHING BEAUTIFUL OUTSIDE?

20___: _____

_____

_____

_____

• ◆ •

20___: _____

_____

_____

_____

• ◆ •

20___: _____

_____

_____

_____

• ◆ •

❖ December ❖

WHEN WAS THE LAST TIME
YOU SAW BEAUTY IN ANOTHER HUMAN?

20___: _____

_____

_____

_____

• ◆ •

20___: _____

_____

_____

_____

• ◆ •

20___: _____

_____

_____

_____

• ◆ •

❖ December ❖

MOST RECENT THING
YOU DID THAT YOU REGRETTED.

20___: _____

_____

_____

_____

•◆•

20___: _____

_____

_____

_____

•◆•

20___: _____

_____

_____

_____

•◆•

WHO DO YOU NEED TO CALL AND SAY "I'M SORRY" TO?

20__: _____

_____

_____

_____

•◆•

20__: _____

_____

_____

_____

•◆•

20__: _____

_____

_____

_____

•◆•

❖ December ❖

WHO CAN YOU CALL AND SAY "I LOVE YOU" TO?

20__: _____

_____

_____

_____

•◆•

20__: _____

_____

_____

_____

•◆•

20__: _____

_____

_____

_____

•◆•

IF GOD WERE SITTING NEXT TO YOU RIGHT NOW, WHAT WOULD YOU ASK HIM?

20__: _____

_____

_____

_____

• ◆ •

20__: _____

_____

_____

_____

• ◆ •

20__: _____

_____

_____

_____

• ◆ •

❖ December ❖

WHERE DO YOU SEE
LIGHT IN THE DARK WORLD?

20__: _____

_____

_____

_____

• ◆ •

20__: _____

_____

_____

_____

• ◆ •

20__: _____

_____

_____

_____

• ◆ •

❖ December ❖

LAST TIME YOU INTERACTED WITH A WIDOW.

20__: _____

_____

_____

_____

•◆•

20__: _____

_____

_____

_____

•◆•

20__: _____

_____

_____

_____

•◆•

10 ❖ December ❖

**LAST HOMELESS PERSON
YOU DID SOMETHING KIND TOWARDS.**

20__: _____

_____

_____

_____

•◆•

20__: _____

_____

_____

_____

•◆•

20__: _____

_____

_____

_____

•◆•

❖ December ❖ 11

LAST TIME YOU READ YOUR BIBLE IN PUBLIC.

20__: _____

_____

_____

_____

• ◆ •

20__: _____

_____

_____

_____

• ◆ •

20__: _____

_____

_____

_____

• ◆ •

12 ❖ December ❖

HOW WELL DID YOU SMILE TO OTHERS TODAY?

20__: _____

_____

_____

_____

•◆•

20__: _____

_____

_____

_____

•◆•

20__: _____

_____

_____

_____

•◆•

ON A SCALE OF 1-10,
DID YOUR WORDS EDIFY OTHERS TODAY?

20___: _____

_____

_____

_____

•◆•

20___: _____

_____

_____

_____

•◆•

20___: _____

_____

_____

_____

•◆•

14 ❖ December ❖

HOW WAS YOUR THOUGHT LIFE TODAY?

20___: _____
_____
_____
_____

•◆•

20___: _____
_____
_____
_____

•◆•

20___: _____
_____
_____
_____

•◆•

HOW MUCH SCREEN TIME DID YOU SPEND THIS WEEK?

20__: _____

_____

_____

_____

•◆•

20__: _____

_____

_____

_____

•◆•

20__: _____

_____

_____

_____

•◆•

16 ❖ December ❖

DID YOU USE YOUR EYES TO SEE GOD HONORING THINGS TODAY?

20__: _____

_____

_____

_____

•◆•

20__: _____

_____

_____

_____

•◆•

20__: _____

_____

_____

_____

•◆•

❖ December ❖ 17

**WHAT VICE ARE YOU TURNING TO,
TO NUMB YOUR PAIN IN THIS SEASON?**

20__: _____

_____

_____

_____

•◆•

20__: _____

_____

_____

_____

•◆•

20__: _____

_____

_____

_____

•◆•

18 ❖ December ❖

DID YOU PRAY TODAY?

20__: _____

_____

_____

_____

●◆●

20__: _____

_____

_____

_____

●◆●

20__: _____

_____

_____

_____

●◆●

❖ December ❖ 19

WHAT ARE YOU DREAMING ABOUT THAT YOU HAVEN'T SHARED WITH ANYONE YET?

20__: _____

_____

_____

_____

• ◆ •

20__: _____

_____

_____

_____

• ◆ •

20__: _____

_____

_____

_____

• ◆ •

 ❖ December ❖

CONSIDER THREE WAYS
YOU CAN GIVE SACRIFICIALLY THIS WEEK.

20__: _____

_____

_____

_____

•◆•

20__: _____

_____

_____

_____

•◆•

20__: _____

_____

_____

_____

•◆•

THIS YEAR WAS VICTORIOUS BECAUSE _____.

20___: _____

_____

_____

_____

•◆•

20___: _____

_____

_____

_____

•◆•

20___: _____

_____

_____

_____

•◆•

 ❖ **December** ❖

WHAT THREE THINGS WOULD YOU CHANGE ABOUT THIS LAST YEAR?

20___: _____

_____

_____

_____

• ◆ •

20___: _____

_____

_____

_____

• ◆ •

20___: _____

_____

_____

_____

• ◆ •

❖ December ❖ **23**

WHAT ONE RELATIONSHIP DO YOU RESOLVE TO BUILD UP NEXT YEAR?

20__: _____

_____

_____

_____

• ◆ •

20__: _____

_____

_____

_____

• ◆ •

20__: _____

_____

_____

_____

• ◆ •

 ❖ December ❖

WHO DID YOU MENTOR THIS LAST YEAR?

20__: _____

_____

_____

_____

• ◆ •

20__: _____

_____

_____

_____

• ◆ •

20__: _____

_____

_____

_____

• ◆ •

❖ December ❖ 25

NAME ONE PERSON IN YOUR LIFE RIGHT NOW WHO NEEDS TO HEAR ABOUT GOD'S LOVE.

20___: _____

_____

_____

_____

●◆●

20___: _____

_____

_____

_____

●◆●

20___: _____

_____

_____

_____

●◆●

 **❖ December ❖**

BIGGEST REGRET OF THE LAST YEAR.

20__: _____

_____

_____

_____

• ◆ •

20__: _____

_____

_____

_____

• ◆ •

20__: _____

_____

_____

_____

• ◆ •

❖ December ❖ 27

WHAT HABIT DO YOU NEED TO DROP STARTING RIGHT NOW?

20__: _____

_____

_____

_____

•◆•

20__: _____

_____

_____

_____

•◆•

20__: _____

_____

_____

_____

•◆•

28 ❖ December ❖

ON A SCALE OF 1-10, RATE THIS LAST YEAR.

20__: _____

_____

_____

_____

•◆•

20__: _____

_____

_____

_____

•◆•

20__: _____

_____

_____

_____

•◆•

❖ December ❖

NAME THREE THINGS YOU ARE DEEPLY THANKFUL FOR THIS YEAR.

20__: _____

_____

_____

_____

•◆•

20__: _____

_____

_____

_____

•◆•

20__: _____

_____

_____

_____

•◆•

30 ❖ December ❖

WHICH BIBLE PASSAGE IMPACTED YOU THE MOST THIS LAST YEAR?

20__: _____

_____

_____

_____

• ◆ •

20__: _____

_____

_____

_____

• ◆ •

20__: _____

_____

_____

_____

• ◆ •

❖ December ❖ 31

WHAT'S YOUR NEW YEAR'S RESOLUTION?

20___: _____

_____

_____

_____

● ◆ ●

20___: _____

_____

_____

_____

● ◆ ●

20___: _____

_____

_____

_____

● ◆ ●

ABOUT THE AUTHOR

Lina AbuJamra is the founder of Living With Power Ministries. She is a pediatric emergency room doctor by profession and is passionate about empowering people with biblical truth. A popular Bible teacher, blogger, and conference speaker, she is the author of several books including *Thrive* and *The Daily Dose:365 Days to a Healthy Soul*.

She reaches listeners through weekly podcasts and a daily Morning Minutes devotional and is engaged in providing medical care for Syrian refugees in the Middle East. You can hear Lina on Moody Radio hosting Today's Single Christian. Lina is single and calls Chicago home.

For additional information go to:
www.livingwithpower.org.